" I gave my love a red, red nose "

Poems About Feelings

Chosen by Gervase Phinn

W
FRANKLIN WATTS
LONDON • SYDNEY

First published in 2001 by
Franklin Watts
96 Leonard Street
London
EC2A 4XD

Franklin Watts Australia
56 O'Riordan Street
Alexandria
NSW 2015

© In this anthology Gervase Phinn 2001

A CIP catalogue record for this book is available
from the British Library.

ISBN 0 7496 4086 3

Series Editor: Louise John
Designer: Robert Walster

Dewey Classification 821.008

Printed in Hong Kong

Acknowledgments

The editor and publishers gratefully acknowledge permission to reproduce the following
copyright material.

'I Gave My Love a Red, Red Nose' and 'Cupboard Love' by Richard Edwards, from 'The
House That Caught a Cold' published by Viking 1991. © Richard Edwards. Reprinted by
permission of the author.
'The Friday Night Smell' by Marc Matthews. © Marc Matthews. Reprinted by permission
of the author.
'Autobiographia Literaria' by Frank O'Hara, from 'Selected Poems'. Reprinted by
permission of Carcanet Press Limited.
'Grandchild' by Ann Bonner, from 'Them and Us' compiled by Jennifer Curry, in 1993. ©
Ann Bonner. Reprinted by permission of the author.
'Friends' by Elizabeth Jennings, from 'Collected Poems' published by Carcanet Press.
Reprited by permission of David Higham Associates Limited.
'Give Yourself a Hug' by Grace Nichols, from 'Give Yourself A Hug' Copyright © Grace
Nichols, 1994. Reprinted by permission of Curtis Brown Limited, London on behalf of
Grace Nichols.
'In Case You're Wondering' by Max Fatchen. Reprinted by permission of John Johnson
(Authors' Agent) Limited.
'First Loves' by Rowena Somerville, from 'The Martians Have Taken My Brother' by
Rowena Somerville, published by Hutchinson. Used by permission of The Random House
Group Limited.
'Mother to Son' by Langston Hughes, from 'Collected Poems' published by Vintage.
Reprinted by permission of David Higham Associates Limited.
'The Irreplaceable Mum' by Brian Patten, from 'Thawing Frozen Frogs' published by
Viking in 1990. Copyright © Brian Patten 1990. Reproduced by permission of the author
c/o Rogers, Coleridge & White Limited, 20 Powis Mews, London W11 1JN.
'Harry Pushed Her' by Peter Thabit Jones. © Peter Thabit Jones. Reprinted by permission
of the author.
'On A Country Walk In A Very Thick Mist' by John Rice. © John Rice. Reprinted by
permission of the author.
'Airmail to a Dictionary' by Lemn Sissay, from 'Doin Mi Ed In' published by Macmillan.
Reprinted by permission of David Higham Associates Limited.
'Alphabet of Love' by Christine Bentley, from 'Lizard Over Ice'. © Christine Bentley.
Reprinted by permission of the author.

Every effort has been made to trace copyright, but if any omissions have been made,
please let us know in order that this may be corrected in the next edition.

Picture Credits

Jade Albert/VCL/Telegraph Colour Library: 30-31
W. Aldridge/Robert Harding PL: cover, 1, 2
Juliette Antoine/Oredia/Retna: 16
B. Binzen/Corbis Stockmarket: 8
Bill Hickey/Image Bank: 12-13
Index/Crejun/PowerstockZefa: 14
Joff Lee/ABPL: 7
Lew Long/Corbis Stockmarket: 23
Romilly Lockyer/Image Bank: 15
Pictor: 20-21
Allan G. Potts/Bruce Coleman Collection: 9
Alain Proust/Cephas: 10/11
Tony Anderson/Stock Directory: 4
Norbert Schafer/Corbis Stockmarket: 25
Michael Shay/VCL/Telegraph Colour Library: 17
George Shelley/Corbis Stockmarket: 29
Stockfood/Cephas: 6
Craig Tuttle/Corbis Stockmarket: 26
Ariel Skelley/The Stock Market: 19

Contents

Secret Love

'Oh tell me, tell me, Lizzie, please
Just what did Jason say.
I know he told you not to tell
But tell me anyway.
When he looks across the room
I go weak at the knees.
Do you think he's going to ask me out?
Oh tell me, Lizzie, please.
Did he say he liked me best,
Or does he like Louise,
Or is it Sue or Jane or Pam,
Oh tell me, Lizzie, please.
I've got to know what Jason said,
Oh, Liz don't be a tease.
I promise I won't say a word
Oh tell me, Lizzie, please.'
'Well can you keep a secret?'
Asked Lizzie, with a sigh,
'Of course I can,' her friend replied,
And Liz said, 'So can I!'

Gervase Phinn

I Gave My Love a Red Red Nose

I gave my love a red red nose
By accident. You see,
While sniffing at the red red rose,
She woke a sleeping bee.

Richard Edwards

5

Cupboard Crush

'Tomato, why do you lie there,
Sighing such desperate sighs?
What's wrong?' asks the soft-hearted lettuce,
And the blushing tomato replies:
'I have fallen in love with King Edward –
Those eyes, those eyes, those eyes!'

Richard Edwards

Beautiful Soup

Beautiful Soup, so rich and green,
Waiting in a hot tureen!
Who for such dainties would not stoop?
Soup of the evening, beautiful Soup!

Soup of the evening, beautiful Soup!
    Beau-ootiful Soo-oop!
    Beau-ootiful Soo-oop!
Soo-oop of the e-e-evening,
    Beautiful, beautiful Soup!

Beautiful Soup! Who cares for fish,
Game, or any other dish?
Who would not give all else for two
Pennyworth only of beautiful Soup?
Pennyworth only of beautiful Soup?
    Beau-ootiful Soo-oop!
    Beau-ootiful Soo-oop!
Soo-oop of the e-e-evening,
    Beautiful, beauti-FUL SOUP!

Lewis Carroll

Autobiographia Literaria

When I was a child
I played by myself in a
corner of the schoolyard
all alone.

I hated dolls and I
hated games, animals were
not friendly and birds
flew away.

If anyone was looking
for me I hid behind a
tree and cried out 'I am
an orphan.'

And here I am, the
centre of all beauty!
writing these poems!
Imagine!

Frank O'Hara

These Have I Loved

These have I loved:
  White plates and cups, cleaning-gleaming,
Ringed with blue lines; and feathery, faery dust;
Wet roofs beneath the lamp-light; the strong crust
Of friendly bread; and many-tasting food;
Rainbows; and the blue bitter smoke of wood;
And radiant raindrops couching in cool flowers;
And flowers themselves, that sway through sunny hours,
Dreaming of moths that drink them under the moon ...
Sweet water's dimpling laugh from tap or spring;
Holes in the ground; and voices that do sing;
Voices in laughter, too; and body's pain.

Rupert Brooke

The Friday Night Smell

I love the
friday night
smell of
mammie baking
bread – creeping
up to me in
bed, and tho
zzzz I'll fall
asleep, before I
even get a
bite – when
morning come,
you can bet
I'll meet a
kitchen table
laden with
bread, still
warm and fresh
salt bread
sweet bread
crisp and brown
& best of all
coconut buns
THAT's why
I love the
friday night
smell of mammie
baking bread

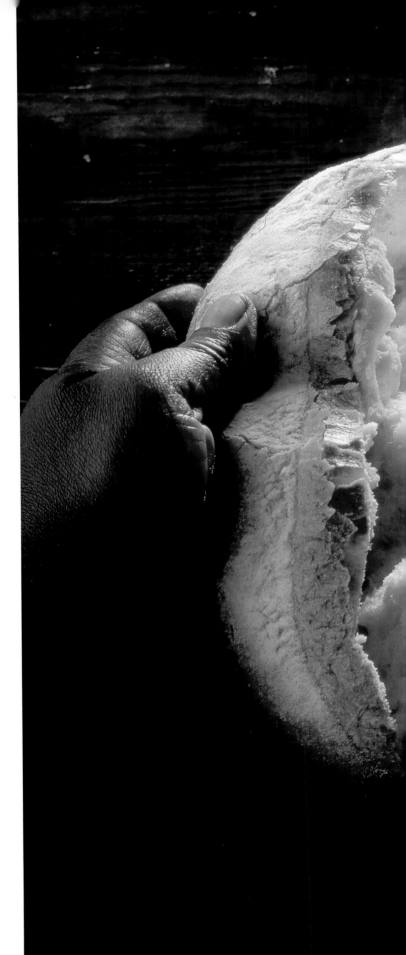

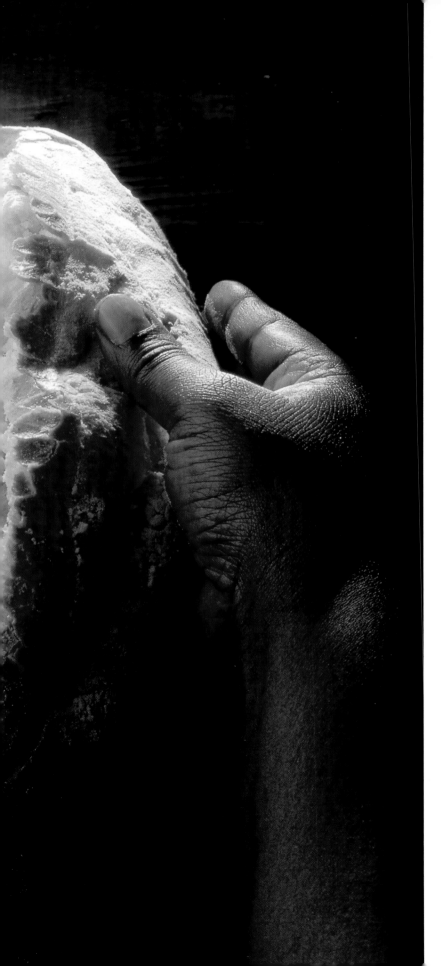

putting me to
sleep, dreaming
of jumping from
the highest branch
of the jamoon tree
into the red water
creek
beating carlton
run & catching
the biggest fish
in the world
plus, getting
the answers right
to every single
sum
that every day
in my dream
begins and ends
with the friday
night smell of
mammie baking
bread, and
coconut buns
of course.

Marc Matthews

Grandchild

You are here.
Filling each room
with your laughter.
When you arrive
the quiet walls come
alive with the sound
of your voice.

Outside the dew
bloom of morning.
Brittle leaves fallen
with autumn take on
a new meaning.
The garden, a little
forlorn at this time
of year gives an ear to
the life that you bring.
Wakes up for a while.
Remembers the spring.

Stars now gleaming.
Moon streaming bright
through the shutters
of night hears your soft
snoring. Your mutters
of dreams as I write.
A storm wind is rising.
While it blows wild
sleep, my grandchild.

Ann Bonner

Oath of Friendship

Shang ya!
I want to be your friend
For ever and ever without break or decay.
When the hills are all flat
And the rivers are all dry,
When it lightens and thunders in winter,
When it rains and snows in summer,
When Heaven and Earth mingle –
Not till then will I part from you.

Anon (China)

Friends

I fear it's very wrong of me,
And yet I must admit,
When someone offers friendship
I want the *whole* of it.
I don't want everybody else
To share my friends with me.
At least, I want *one* special one,
Who, indisputably

Likes me more than all the rest,
Who's always on my side,
Who never cares what others say,
Who lets me come and hide
Within his shadow, in his house –
It doesn't matter where –
Who lets me simply be myself,
Who's always, *always* there.

Elizabeth Jennings

Give Yourself a Hug

Give yourself a hug
when you feel unloved

Give yourself a hug
when people put on airs
to make you feel a bug

Give yourself a hug
when everyone seems to give you
a cold-shoulder shrug

Give yourself a hug –
a big big hug

And keep on singing,
'Only one in a million like me
Only one in a million-billion-
thrillion-zillion like me.'

Grace Nichols

16

In Case You're Wondering ...

I want for Christmas ...
... Let me see ...
I want your spending
Time with me.

I want your jokes
Around my place,
And how you pull
A funny face.

I want your laughter
And your chat.
I want your smile
I DO want that.

I want your eyes
Of dancing blue.
I want a nice
Fat present too.

Max Fatchen

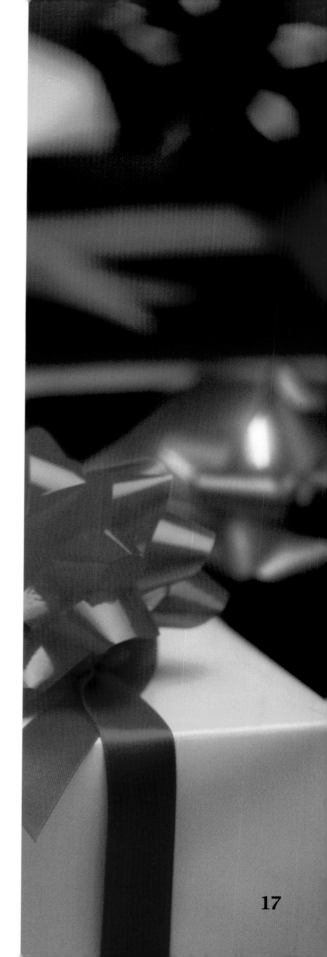

First Loves

I'm in love, I am, with Martin,
though I've been too shy to speak,
but I love his curly lashes,
and the freckles on his cheek,
although sometimes I love Phillip,
'cos he stands so tall and strong,
and he tells those awful stories
that just carry you along,
and on the bus I saw a boy
who turned me to a wreck,
though I sat behind him just the once,
and I only saw his neck,
and I did love Mr. Collins,
'cos he's always really kind,
but he's old and bald and married,
so I've put him from my mind,
and I really liked that footballer
who scored and won the cup,
but I couldn't stand the football,
so I had to give him up,
and you know that gorgeous singer,
well, I couldn't eat my tea,
'cos he looked into the camera,
and I know he winked at me,
and I love that man on telly
who does all the fiddly bits,
in between the proper programmes,

but my mother says that it's
not the real, true thing at all,
it's puppy love, and so
I'll fancy someone else tomorrow,
but I say
What do mothers know?

Rowena Somerville

The Irreplaceable Mum

If you were a crack in the mirror,
If you were a flea on a cat,
If you were a slug in a jug,
I'd still love you, I wouldn't mind that.

If you were a smudge on a picture
Or an opera singer struck dumb,
If you were a pain in the neck then
You'd still be my very best chum.

If you were a fly in a pizza,
If you were a difficult sum,
Even if you were humpy and grumpy
You'd still be irreplaceable, Mum.

Brian Patten

20

Mother to Son

Well, son, I'll tell you:
Life for me ain't been no crystal stair.
It's had tacks in it,
And splinters,
And boards torn up,
And places with no carpet on the floor –
Bare.
But all the time
I'se been a-climbin' on,
And reachin' landin's,
And turnin' corners,
And sometimes goin' in the dark
Where there ain't been no light.
So boy, don't you turn back.
Don't you set down on the steps
'Cause you finds it's kinder hard.
Don't you fall now –
For I'se still goin', honey,
I'se still climbin',
And life for me ain't been no crystal stair.

Langston Hughes

Harry Pushed Her

Harry pushed her;
He pushed her around;
He pushed his sister.
Before school, after school;
On weekends.
He pushed his sister;
He had no friends.
He pushed her: school holidays
And Christmas time.
The children always
Sang their made-up rhyme:
'Harry push her! Push her quick!
Harry push her! Make her sick!'
Harry pushed her without strain:
Through snow, sunshine, wind and rain.
She smiled strangely
And never said a word.
He pushed her for years –
It was so absurd.
Harry was twelve;
His sister twenty-three.
Harry never had a childhood like me.
Harry pushed her without a care;
He pushed his sister in her wheelchair.

Peter Thabit Jones

My True Love

On Monday, Monday,
      My True Love said to me,
'I've brought you this nice pumpkin;
      I picked it off a tree!'

On Tuesday, Tuesday,
      My True Love said to me,
'Look – I've brought you sand tarts;
      I got them by the sea.'

On Wednesday, Wednesday,
      My True Love said to me,
'I've caught you this white polar bear;
      It came from Tennessee.'

On Thursday, Thursday,
      My True Love said to me,
'This singing yellow butterfly
      I've all for you, from me.'

On Friday, Friday,
      My True Love said to me,
'Here's a long-tailed guinea pig;
      It's frisky as can be.'

On Saturday, Saturday,
      To my True Love I said,
'You have not told me ONE TRUE THING,
      So you I'll never wed!'

Ivy O Eastwick

On a Country Walk in a Very Thick Mist

On a country walk in a very thick mist
My girlfriend asked if I'd give her a kiss,
    But I missed her lips
    Because of the fog
And I kissed her little one-eyed dog.

John Rice

I Am Blind But I Can See

I see with my ears.
I hear the leaves in the tall trees, whispering in the night.
I hear the sea, dark and deep, and the splash of the
dolphin's leap.
I hear the flames crackling and the window frames
rattling in the wind.
I see with my ears.

I see with my nose.
I smell the blossoms pearly grey and hay new mown.
I smell the ploughed earth, cows in the byre, the smoky fire.
I smell Grandpa's pipe, Gran's lavender room and mum's
faint perfume.
I see with my nose.

I see with my mouth.
I taste the strong black coffee and the thick brown toffee
between my teeth.
I taste the yellow of the lemon, the green of the melon
and the red of the tomato.
I taste the orange of the carrot, the purple of the plum,
the gold of the sun on my face.
I see with my mouth.

I see with my hands.
I feel the sharp edges, slippery floors, smooth ledges.
I feel lemonade in cold canisters, hard wooden banisters.
I feel hands to hold, arms on shoulders, faces to touch.
I see with my hands.

Ruth Meachin

27

Airmail to a Dictionary

Black is... the shawl of the night
Secure from sharp paranoic light

Black is... the pupil of the eye
Putting colour in the seas skin and earthen sky

Black is... the oil of the engine
On which this whole world's depending

Black is... light years of space
Holding on its little finger this human race

Black is... the colour of ink
That makes the history books we print

Black is... the army. Wars in the night
Putting on the black to hide the white

Black is... the colour of cold
Giving work to the miners warmth to the old

Black is... the shade of the tree
Sharp in definition against inequality

Black is... the eclipse of the sun
Displaying its power to everyone.

Black is... the ink from a history
That shall redefine the dictionary

Black on black is black is black is
Strong as asphalt and tarmac is

Black is a word that I love to see
Black is that, yeah, black is me.

Lemn Sissay

Alphabet of Love

April loves
Barry but he adores
Cheryl who only likes
David with the dark brown eyes
Elsie ignores
Felicity who can't stand
Georgina who really hates
Harriet who is always telling lies!
Ian sits with
Jason and they talk about
Katy who stares through large blue spectacles at
Leonard who she hates!
Maureen shouts at
Noleen for telling all her secrets to
Olivia and
Prudence and all her other mates.
Quentin's pal is
Russell and they come to school together with
Simon and
Timothy and
Uriah on their bikes
Veronica comes in Daddy's Porsche and
Wendy with her grandma and
Xavier, he stays at home and does just as he likes.
Yvonne-Marie for all to see loves only little
Zebedee.

Christine Bentley

Index of First Lines